Planet Plenty

An environmental musical for Key Stage 2

Written by
JANE SMITH

First Published
January 08 in Great Britain by

PUBLISHING

© Jane Smith 2008

ISBN-10: 1-905637-44-6
ISBN-13: 978-1-905637-44-7

Educational Printing Services Limited
Albion Mill, Water Street, Great Harwood, Blackburn BB6 7QR
Telephone: (01254) 882080   Fax: (01254) 882010
E-mail: enquiries@eprint.co.uk   Website: www.eprint.co.uk

First performed by the children of
High Wycombe Primary schools
for the Energize festival, 2006.

Dedicated to the children of
Seer Green CE Combined School.

Includes script, piano score, staging notes, lyric sheets,
links to QCA schemes of work,
and original choreography by Tracey Howkins.

Index . . .

SONGS

Staging Suggestions . . .

The Show

'Planet Plenty' is a versatile show that is designed to be adapted to suit the needs of your school. There are 40 speaking roles, but these could be reduced by allowing only a few children to take the narrating responsibility. Or, you could extend the opportunities by adding more dialogue if you wanted, or by allowing the children to improvise scenes instead of using the narrators. The twelve songs could be sung by all the cast, but there are many opportunities for smaller groups of children to shine, whether through singing part of the song as a solo, playing instruments and junk percussion to accompany the singing, or by dancing in the instrumental sections. The show is also suitable to be performed by a number of schools combining for a festival or special event. In this case, each school could take responsibility for a particular dance or song. Links to QCA guidelines, and choreography ideas by Tracey Howkins can be found at the back of the book.

The Music

The songs have been written to be accessible to all children, whether beginner singers or those with lots of experience. Almost every song could be performed simply in unison, using only the Voice 1 part, but there are opportunities to stretch the children by adding extra vocal lines. Many of the songs could be used to demonstrate different teaching points covered in the music curriculum, and parts of the ongoing units of work, Units 8 and 15, are addressed with every song. Full educational notes are shown at the back of the book. The song *Drip, Drip* is written to include pitched classroom percussion, and *Recycle* uses junk percussion that can be made by the children, or they can use found materials. Any extra percussion played by the children to accompany the singing would also work well. The children could be encouraged to move with the songs, making up their own actions to support the singing. Many of the songs have a driving rhythm, which would be supported well by guitar and drums if performing with a live accompaniment.

Staging

'Planet Plenty' can be performed in as simple or as complicated a way as suits your school. It would be good to have a difference between Planet Plenty and Planet Pleasant. This could be achieved just by changing the sign at the front of the stage, or it could be made more convincing by changing the lighting, or even changing parts of the set. The Action Squad's rocket could be a lifesize one that the children move around the stage, or you could have a model rocket on a stick moved by one of the children. The few props needed, such as the Weather Girl's map and the Royal Gardener's newspaper, could all be easily made by the children in school.

Cast List . . . (with costume suggestions)

Plentarians

King	Wears a shiny cloak and crown, with cool shades.
Queen	Could wear cloak, crown and tutu with stripy tights.
Courtiers	All wear shiny clothes from man made materials. Could be made from bin bags.
Princess	Spoilt, and always wears pink. The brighter the better.
Princess's friends	Also in pink.
Royal Weather Girl	Smartly dressed, with a pointer for showing the weather on the screen.
Royal Gardener	Wellies, big jumper and a hat.
Animals	Use masks or coloured clothes to show different types.
Mayor	A big hat to show how important he or she is.
Royal Scientists	White coats, clip boards, glasses, bald head wigs.
Action Squad	Tracksuits and trainers. Or PE kit.
Factory owners	Dark clothes with bowler hats.
Children	School uniform.

Pleasantites

Groups	All the Pleasantites wear clothes made from natural materials, in muted colours. Could wear robes with sandals.
President	Chain of office to distinguish from the group of Pleasantites.
Chancellor	Different badge of office.
Minister for Energy and Councillors	Tie dye clothes, long hair wigs.

Narrators

Smart clothes, maybe school uniform with a tie.

Props needed

Planet Plenty sign
Map for the Weather Girl
Newspaper for the Royal Gardener
Parachute, for the scientists to use to pretend to be the monster in the CO_2 monster song.

Rocket
Planet Pleasant sign
Rubbish to use as junk percussion

Play Script . . .

Song 1 : Planet Plenty

(Big sign saying 'Planet Plenty' put up on the stage.)

Narrator 1   Let us tell you about Planet Plenty. It is a small planet; the Plentarian spaceships can whizz round it in an afternoon. They think they have everything here! They live in the most up to date plastic houses, which they create in big factories on the other side of the planet. They all have swimming pools in their gardens.

Narrator 2   Everyone has their own spaceship, which the children learn to drive at the age of 8. Their favourite way of spending time is to go shopping. They like to always have new things, so when they're fed up with their old ones they throw them away, and the breeze carries them to the big rubbish site near the factories.

Narrator 3   Their glorious King, Percy Plenty rules over them, with his exquisite Queen, Penelope Plenty. Their motto is 'Live for Today', and they say 'why shouldn't we, when everything here is so perfect?' But is it?

(Enter King with his courtiers, with towels around shoulders, after having been swimming, whistling the Planet Plenty song.)

King   Well, I've said it before, and I'll say it again – we are the luckiest people in the galaxy.   Did you know, I've heard that on some planets not everyone has their own swimming pool?

(Gasps from courtiers and chorus)

I know!

(Looks around)

Hang on a minute – there's something not right here! There are two things not right here!

(Further gasps from courtiers and chorus)

King	The sun is so strong that it's making my eyes hurt through my shades! And look at my lawn – it's not green any more, it's going brown! What is going on?

(Confusion from courtiers and chorus – hold horrified pose)

Narrator 4	And it was true. The day had been so hot that the court had all been sunburnt, and the lawn had started to dry up. So the King sent for the obvious person to help in this crisis – the Royal Weather Girl.
Royal Weather Girl (RWG)	*(Simpering and gesticulating at a map which shows large suns all over the planet.)* Good morning! Your Majesty, if we take a look at the map, we can see that weather-wise we're going to have an absolutely glorious day today. Then there'll be a mild start to the day tomorrow, and it won't cloud over a little later. Nor will there be even the odd spot of rain. In fact, for most of us it will be an absolutely glorious day again tomorrow! Through the evening it will remain hot, and you need to apply your sunscreen, as the UV levels are going to remain high. If we're to take a look at our long range forecasts, we will see that it will stay scorching next week, next month and next year!
King	So are you saying the weather's getting hotter?
RWG	Well, Your Majesty, here's a summary. Yes. The weather's getting hotter.
King	How has this happened? Why is our weather changing?
RWG	Well, it's funny you should ask, but I've just been watching Good Morning Planet Plenty, and they were saying that something called Global Warming has started, and it seems to be particularly bad on our planet.

(Gasps of horror)

King	Why? What does that mean?
RWG	Nobody really knows, but it looks like all the weather's going to change, 'cos everything's getting hotter.

Song 2 : The Heat is On

(Exit King and courtiers, shaking heads. Enter Queen and her courtiers.)

Queen   I do love our Friday picnics. Do you?

All *(bowing)*   Yes, Your Majesty.

Queen   They were a very good idea of mine, don't you think?

All *(bowing)*   Yes, Your Majesty.

Queen   I like to sit under the trees and look at my lovely pink plastic palace, and be pleased that I am the best Queen of the best planet there is.

All *(bowing)*   Yes, Your Majesty.

(Queen looks around her imperiously)

Queen   But today there's something wrong!

(Worried noises from courtiers and chorus)

What's happened to the trees? Where have all the leaves gone? Why do they look such a funny colour? What's going on?

(Confusion from courtiers and chorus – hold another horrified pose)

Narrator 5   And it was true. Instead of being a healthy green, the trees looked dark and diseased. The leaves had fallen to the ground, and no new ones were growing. Instead of giving shade, their branches were stark and bare against the sky. So the Queen sent for the obvious person to help in this sort of crisis, the Royal Gardener.

(Enter Royal Gardener, in wellies and TV gardener outfit.)

Royal Gardener   Your Majesty, I'm afraid that there is nothing much I can do to help you. Even a new water feature won't make much difference. I could paint the trees blue if you wanted?

Queen   Don't be ridiculous! I want to know what has happened! What has made our lovely trees look like this? Have they got a disease?

Royal Gardener produces oversized copy of the InterGalactic Express newspaper, with large headline saying Acid Rain Kills Trees – (opposing back page refers to local football team winning InterGalactic Cup)

Royal Gardener I'm afraid they have, Your Majesty. In the paper, it says that the rain has turned acid, and it is killing all the trees.

(Cries of dismay from courtiers)

Nobody knows what is making it happen, but it seems to be particularly bad here on Planet Plenty.

All No! This can't be true!

Song 3 : Acid Rain Blues

Exit Queen and her courtiers. As narrator speaks, group of citizens and animals enter. Humans take one side of the stage – animals the others. Freeze in talking pose.

Narrator 6 In the market place, the citizens, led by the Mayor, are having a meeting with the animals, led by the Lion. Animals can talk on Planet Plenty, but there isn't as much talking going on as there used to be, because there aren't as many animals as there used to be . . .

Mayor Thank you, our animal friends, for coming to talk with us. We have noticed that we don't see you as often as we used to. Where are the rest of you? Why don't you come into our gardens and parks as you did in the past?

Lion Because this is all there are of us. There are no more animals on Planet Plenty.

Mayor Where have they gone? Surely they're not . . .

Lion The water isn't good to drink any more, and the food tastes bad. The air isn't clean, and we aren't as strong as you. You must be careful.

Mayor What do you mean?

Lion Soon you will be the only ones left. Although we were here first, you will be the last. Help us, before it is too late.

Song 4 : Alone

(As the song continues - as a round - different groups of animals leave the stage, until there are only the humans left. They freeze as the music finishes, then exit.)

Enter the King and Queen, with their courtiers. Royal Princess enters with a group of girlfriends.

Princess   Mummy, Daddy, something terrible has happened!

(King and Queen rush to the Princess's side, along with the girlfriends.)

King   What is it, honey bun? What could have upset you so much?

Queen   Tell us, pumpkin. You must always be happy!

Princess   Well, I was just off to the Royal Disco, and I got in my spaceship, you know, the one I got last weekend, and I got stuck!

All   Stuck?!

Princess   Yes, stuck in a spaceship jam! There were lots of other spaceships flying all over the place, and there wasn't room for me to get through. So I missed the disco!

(All tut as the Princess stamps her foot.)

Princess   It's not fair. I should be able to go as fast as I like, and no-one should get in my way. Surely that's one of the rules on Planet Plenty? Something has got to be done. I think we should build lots more space highways, so that everyone can get around. All this congestion is really annoying me!

Song 5 : Spaceship Jam

Narrator 7   So maybe not everything is as lovely on Planet Plenty as the Plentarians thought. Everyone has a different idea about what should be done to make things better. And, as is normal on the planet, everyone puts their point of view at once.

(All characters argue amongst themselves.)

King and Queen	Stop! This is getting us nowhere.
King	We can't just sit and argue about these things, that isn't helping us at all. I have a very good idea.

(Round of applause and murmurs of hooray from the citizens.)

King	We will send for the Royal Scientists! They spend all their time in their laboratories being clever. I'm sure that they will know whether we should be worrying about these things or not.
Queen	Oh very well done, dear. That was one of your best ideas! *(To the nearest citizen)* Send for the Royal Scientists!

(Citizens pass the request down the line until it goes off the stage. Immediately enter the Royal Scientists)

Royal Scientist 1	Your Majesties. We have been informed that you require our assistance. How can we facilitate your increased comprehension of the present situation, which is causing such anxiety?
Citizens	What?
Royal Scientists	How can we help?
King	Well, before we tell you that, can you show us that you know what you are talking about? How can we trust what you have to say? And tell us using words people who aren't as clever as me might understand!

(Royal Scientists look outraged)

Royal Scientist 2	Let us tell you about ourselves. We spend our lives in laboratories measuring and filtering and experimenting and thinking, so that people not as clever as us have answers for the difficult problems they see all around them.
Queen	And can you come up with some answers for the problems with the weather and the animals and all the other things that are going wrong with the planet?

(Scientists go into a huddle to talk about the problem)

Royal Scientist 1	It gives us enormous satisfaction to convey to you the message that we can reply categorically in the affirmative.
All	What?
Royal Scientists	Yes we can!
Royal Scientist 3	All our problems are caused by too much carbon dioxide, or CO_2 as we like to call it. It is spoiling the atmosphere, and that is what is causing the acid rain, and the changes in the weather, and we think it's what is making the animals die.
Queen	But does it really matter? Should we be bothered?
Royal Scientist 3	If the build up of CO_2 in the atmosphere doesn't stop then eventually the planet will die.
King	So why is there so much CO_2? Who is spoiling the planet for us? I will throw them out of Planet Plenty!
Royal Scientist 3	Well, that's the problem. We don't really know. We can't see who's causing it, so we think it must be a monster.

(Small gasps from the crowd)

A carbon dioxide monster.

(Bigger gasps from the crowd)

We think it's out there, making CO_2 to spoil our planet.

(Loud cries of dismay)

(As song is sung, scientists 'become' the monster using a parachute.)

Song 6 : CO_2 Monster

(Shouts of anger and dismay. Freeze in pose)

Narrator 8	The Plentarians are horrified. A monster that was prepared to pump out carbon dioxide to spoil the planet? This called for someone special to save the planet, and save the day. It called for a team of special people. The Planet Plenty Action Squad!

(Action Squad enter the stage – jumps, cartwheels and somersaults if possible!)

Action Squad Leader	We've heard there's a monster to deal with. We're just the team for the job. There isn't a stronger, braver or cleverer team of people on the planet. Where are we going to?

(Scientists are pointing to a map of the universe, with an arrow pointing to Planet Pleasant)

Royal Scientist 4	You are going to Planet Pleasant. There isn't nearly as much CO_2 in their atmosphere, so they must have defeated the carbon dioxide monster on their planet. Go there, talk to them about it, and they might show you how to catch it.

(Action Squad salutes, then jumps onto a rocket and zooms off stage. Action Squad music again. Then reappears, landing on Planet Pleasant. The squad walks around, sniffing the air. Planet Plenty sign removed, to be replaced with Planet Pleasant sign.)

Narrator 9	So the Action Squad arrives at a planet that is not like Planet Plenty. The Planet Pleasant inhabitants, the Pleasantites, look at the world in a different way. They are watching the Action Squad as they explore their planet.

Action Squad Leader	Well, squad, this is the place. It feels very peculiar here. What is it that's different to back home? It's something about the smell, I think.

Action Squad 1	There isn't a smell! That's what's different, I can't smell rubbish! This planet is much cleaner than ours. Maybe the CO_2 monster has been making smells on Planet Plenty as well as everything else. We must talk to the Pleasantites to get information quickly, so that we can stop it spoiling our planet.

(Pleasantites enter)

President	Welcome. I am the Pleasant President. You are honoured guests on our planet, and we will help you make yourselves at home. To what do we owe the pleasure of your visit?

(As narrators 10 and 11 speak, the two groups shake hands.)

Narrator 10	So the Action Squad explained why they had come. To their surprise, the Pleasantites said that they had never heard of a CO_2 monster, and that they had certainly never fought one.

They preferred not to fight anything, but to live happily on their planet, surrounded by beautiful plants and animals. The Plentarian Action Squad could see that there were many lovely things on this planet that they didn't have at home.

Narrator 11   The Pleasantites then invited the Action Squad to stay whilst their rocket was being refuelled. They showed them where the tap was to pour themselves glasses of water. As they always did at home, the Plentarians let the tap run for a few minutes so that the water was nice and cold.

(Pleasantites are pointing and talking to each other whilst watching the Action Squad let a big fake tap run)

President   My friends, what are you doing? Why are you letting our precious water run down the drain? You should always look after it, otherwise it will run out, and then your planet will be dry and will not be able to support you or your animals.

(Action Squad look at each other guiltily)

(As the song is sung, different groups of pitched percussionists play on xylophones, glockenspiel or metallophones.)

Song 7 : Drip Drip

(New group of Pleasantites enter as first group leave.)

Narrator 12   The Action Squad thought hard about the way they wasted water back at home, whilst they ate their packed lunch. As they always did on Planet Plenty, they left their rubbish on the ground when they had finished, expecting the wind to carry it away. The Pleasantite Chancellor and his friends were horrified.

Chancellor   My friends, what are you doing? You cannot leave your rubbish here. You must live by the three Rs. Reduce, Reuse and Recycle. If *you* cannot use your rubbish again, then it must be sorted and recycled so that you do not waste our planet's resources, not left on the ground where it might injure animals or pollute our environment.

(Action Squad show that they are beginning to understand. Pleasantites pick up the rubbish that had been discarded (coke cans, plastic bottles, copper piping, large water container) and use it to accompany the song and dance with.)

Song 8 : Recycle!

Narrator 13 The Action Squad thought about what they had been told, and wondered whether all the rubbish that they had been throwing away at home had been causing some of their problems. They became very upset, and started pacing up and down, wondering whether all their problems had been of their own making. Maybe there wasn't such a thing as a CO_2 monster after all? Then they were joined by the Pleasantite Minister for Energy, with his councillors.

(Action Squad pace up and down as the hippy like councillors enter.)

Minister for Energy Cool man, it's, like, really groovy that you have all come to our pad. I really dig that you've come to see us, but how come you look so uptight?

(Action Squad continue to pace up and down.)

Minister for Energy Hey chill out dudes. Why are you all being in such a stress? You need to kick back, let it all hang out. Just save energy – that's the way to save your planet.

Narrator 14 So they had guessed right! There wasn't a CO_2 monster. They had been making the carbon dioxide themselves by the way they had been living. They had to start saving energy if they were going to save their planet.

Narrator 15 The Minister told them that just turning off their lights when they weren't in a room, using energy saving light bulbs, and turning down the heating by one degree could reduce how much carbon dioxide they made. They could also help by turning off the TV at the wall instead of using the remote. Just little things would make such a difference.

Song 9 : Save Energy

(Exit Councillors)

Narrator 16 The Action Squad thought sadly about how stupid they had been. The people of their planet had been responsible for all the things that had been going wrong. They thought about all the lights they had been leaving on, all the taps that they had left running, all the rubbish that they had allowed to blow all over their planet. Then they thought about the fuel in their spaceships.

Action Squad 2	Captain, surely our spaceship fuel is energy too? Shouldn't we be thinking about how to save that energy as well?
Action Squad 3	Don't be stupid, how could we get about without our spaceships? I really wonder about you sometimes.
Narrator 17	At that moment, they could hear the whirring of wheels, the spinning of pedals and the tinkling of bells. Before they could move, the Action Squad were almost run over by a group of Pleasantites, all wearing helmets.

(Enter Cyclists)

Cyclist 1	We are the Pleasantite cyclists! We love to cycle! We heard about your problem, and we have come up with a solution. You don't need to use your spaceships for all your journeys. Try pedal power instead!
Cyclist 2	If you use a bicycle, you will get fit, and you won't be harming your planet by using up energy, or by releasing nasty fumes. In fact, whilst you've been here we have converted your spaceships to pedal power, so that you can go home cleanly!

Song 10 : Riding on my bike!

(After the song finishes, the Action Squad wave goodbye from their spaceship, pedalling as they go. Cyclists wave and call goodbye.)

(Planet Pleasant sign is replaced by the Planet Plenty sign.)

(Enter King, Queen, Princess and courtiers. Also enter citizens and animals, and group of children and factory owners.)

Narrator 18	So the Action Squad returned to Planet Plenty, full of excitement about all the new things they had learnt, and looking forward to telling everyone about how they could improve the health of their planet. They got everyone together in the town square, to give them the news. But the meeting did not go as they expected.

(Action Squad enter)

Action Squad Leader	So we need to cut down on our use of spaceships, and use bicycles instead. We must be careful to save energy in our houses and factories. We also need to be careful about how much water we use, and we need to stop churning so much rubbish out onto the planet. And this is for everyone! We must all pay attention and change the way we live!

(Factory owners grumble and complain amongst themselves)

Factory Owner 1	Well I think you have a cheek coming here and telling me how to run my life. I have been running my factory for years like this and no-one has ever before dared to tell me what to do. If I change the way my factory runs, I will lose some of my profit! Why should I?

(Grumbling and shouting from the Factory Owners to the Action Squad. A small child steps through the crowd holding the hand of the lion)

Child	Why shouldn't you? Your factories make lots of the pollution on Planet Plenty. If you don't listen to what these people say, then there won't be a planet for my friends and me in the future. There won't be a planet for the animals either. If you don't change your ways, you'll find yourself in a battle for the planet!
Factory Owner 2	What a foolish child you are. What could you possibly know about how to run a business, or the future of the planet? Run along now, and let me tell the grown ups about why this ridiculous idea couldn't possibly work. You don't need to listen; you wouldn't understand.

(Children group together in indignation, whilst Factory Owners try to persuade the others of their point of view.)

Song 11 : Battle for the Planet

(Song ends in stand off, with both groups opposing each other with clenched fists)

King and Queen	Stop! This is getting us nowhere.
Queen	There is a compromise that would work for all of us. We need a cleaner planet, don't we?

(Shouts of agreement, and the Queen turns to the Factory Owners)

Queen   But you don't want to lose all your money?

(Grumbles of agreement)

Queen   We have to clean up the planet, or else soon we won't be able to live on it. However, if we do, not only will it be nicer for all of us to live in, but also it will attract the tourists from other planets! They could come for their holidays, and bring their money!

(Factory Owners show agreement and understanding)

Queen   This will mean some changes for everyone, but it will be worth it in the end. We must all work together to defeat the CO_2 monsters! They are us!! I am going to start by turning down the heating in the palace.

(All cheer)

King   And I will make sure that all the lights are turned off when there's no-one in the room. From this day forward the motto of Planet Plenty will not be 'live for today'. It will be 'live for tomorrow'!

(More cheers from assembled company)

Song 12 : Live for Tomorrow

Planet Plenty

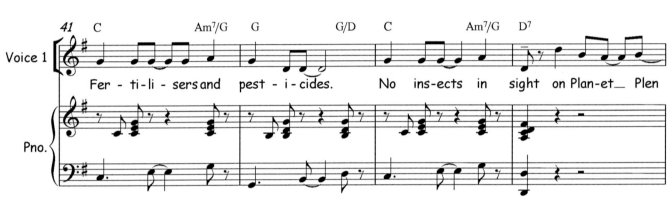

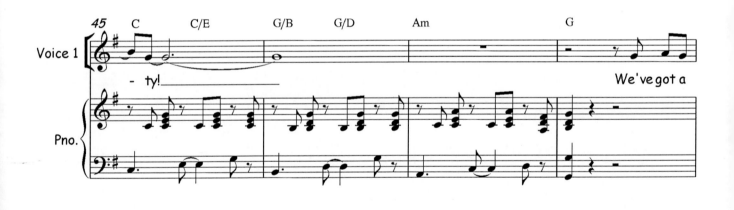

The Heat is On

found, the ext-ra heat is stir-ring up the wea- ther!

The heat is on,_____ and get-ting hot-ter ev-ery

The heat is on,_____ and get-ting hot-ter ev-ery

hour_____ It's get-ting far too hot to play, we'd rath-er lie down in the

hour_____ It's get-ting far too hot to play, we'd rath-er lie down in the

shade, or spend our time und-er a show - er_____ The weath-er's turn-ing in-side

shade, or spend our time und-er a show - er_____ The weath-er's turn-ing in-side

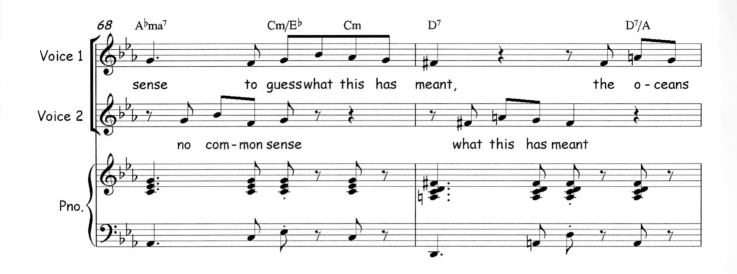

Acid Rain Blues

Alone

41

42

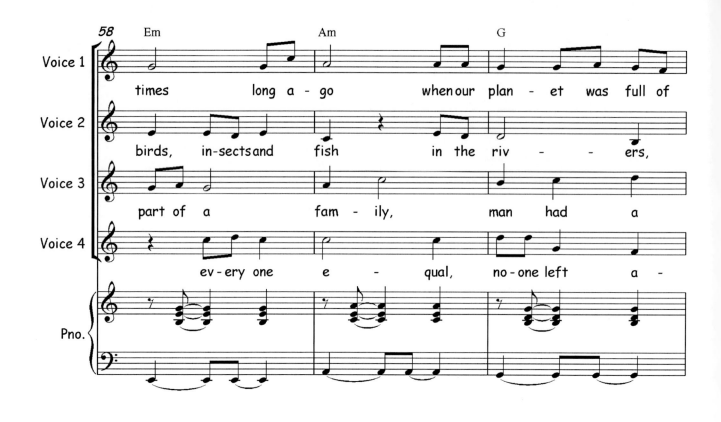

44

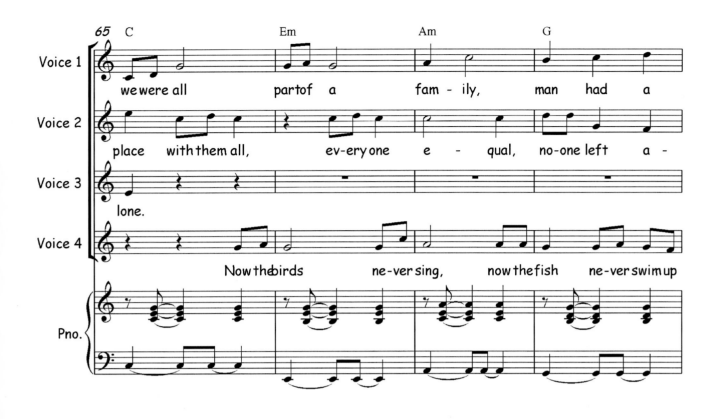

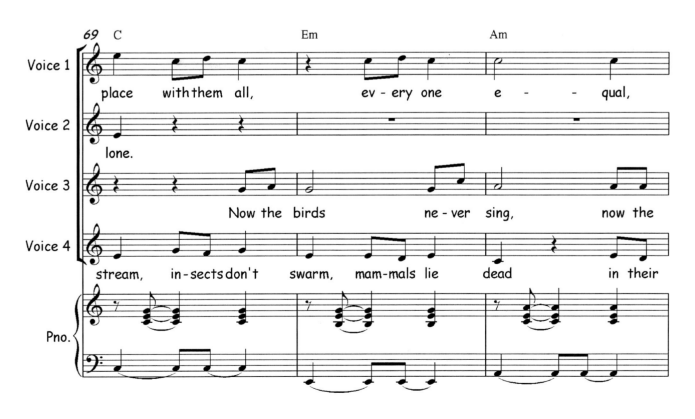

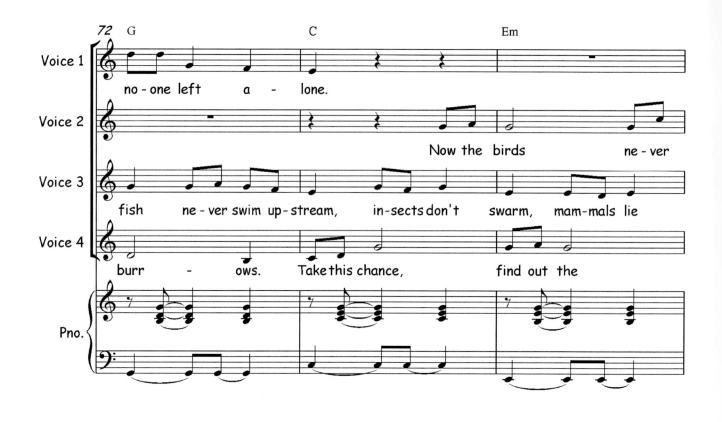

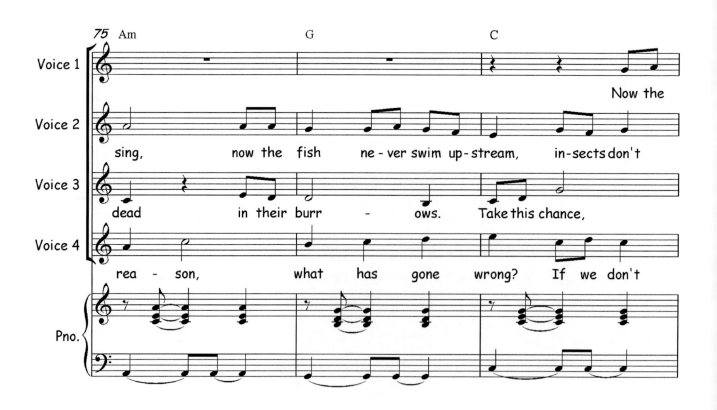

Spaceship Jam

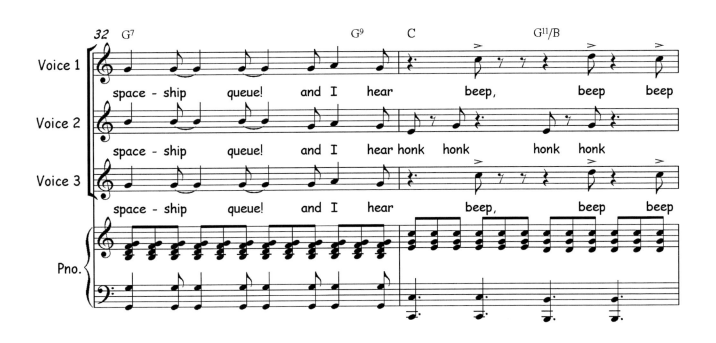

CO$_2$ Monster

Drip Drip

Like a gamelan ♩ = 90

C pentatonic throughout

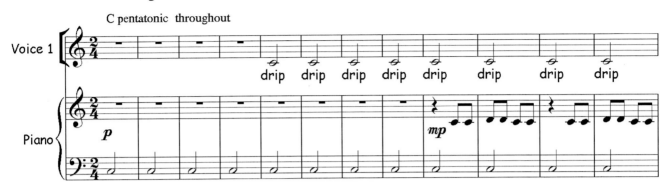

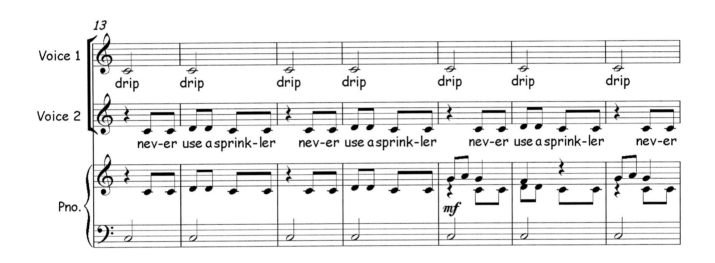

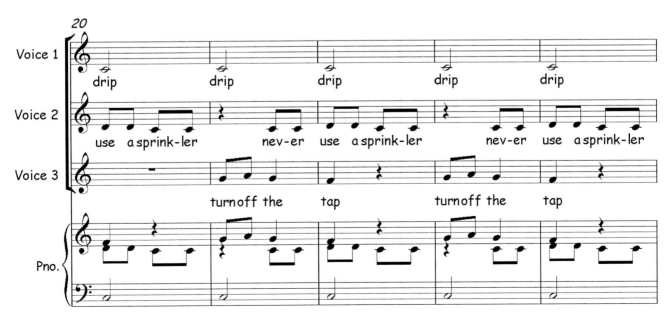

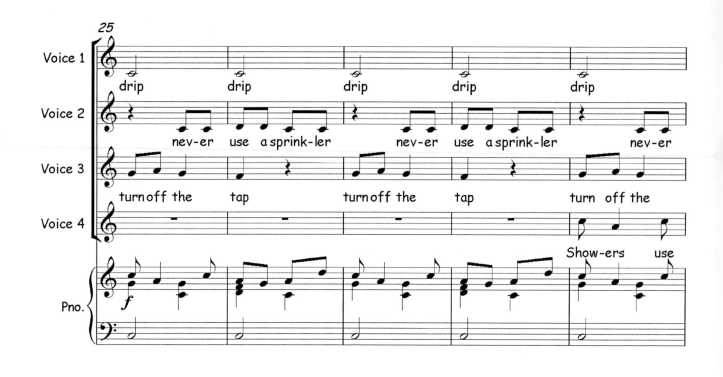

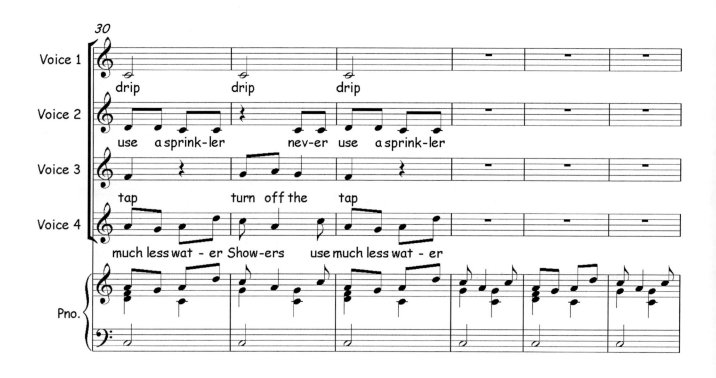

Drip Drip
Pitched percussion parts

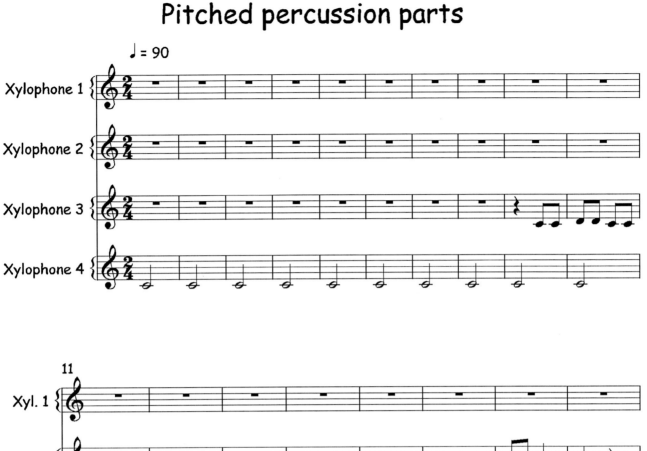

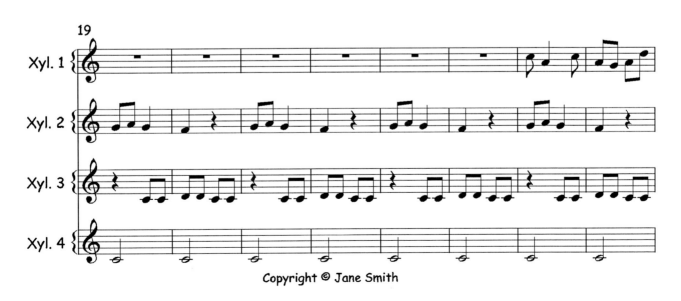

68

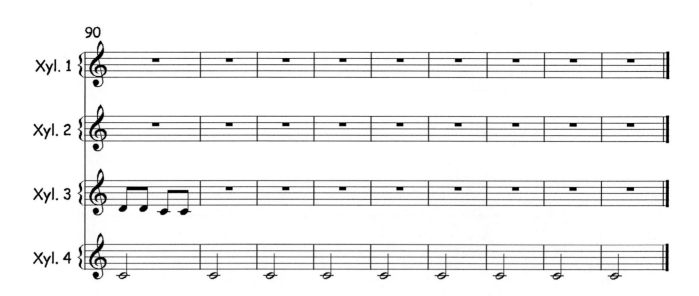

Recycle!

Lyrics (Voice 1): News-pa-pers drink cans, car-tons and vegg-ie peel-ings, cat-a -logues, old mag a -

Lyrics (Voice 1): zines. Plas - - tic bott-les egg box-es pol - y-sty -

Lyrics (Voice 2): Re-cy-cle!

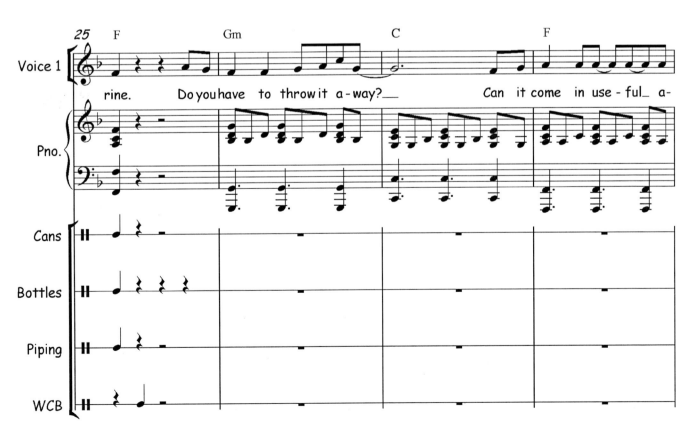

Can it come in use-ful_ a-noth-er day? We can save the plan-et if we

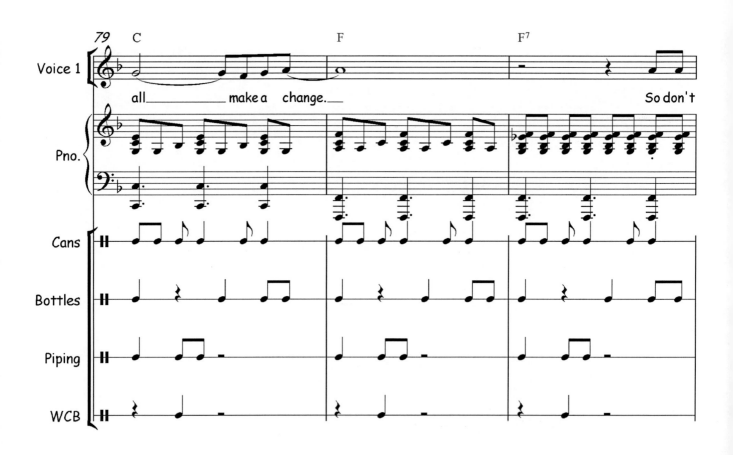

all_____ make a change.___ So don't

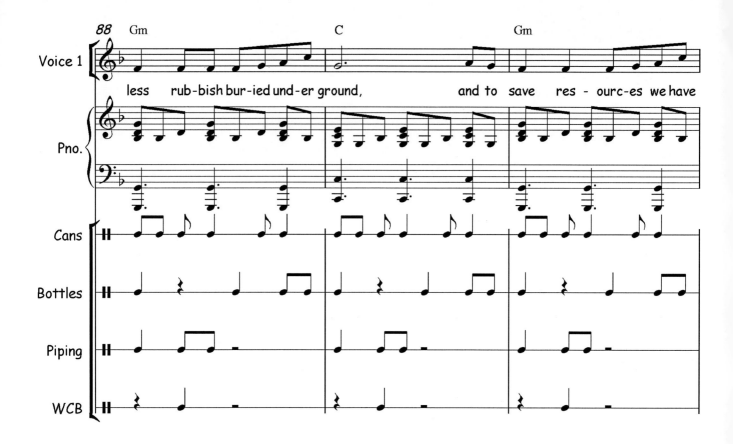

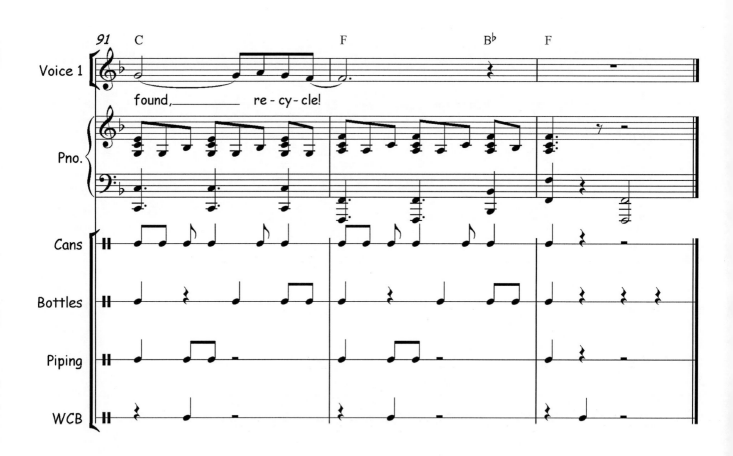

Save Energy

82

Riding on my Bike

Cakewalk ♩ = 146

Ri-ding on my bi- ke!

Ri-ding on my bi- ke! There's

noth-ing like be-ing on my bike with the wind rush-ing pa-st my hair.___ The

fields tear past,'cos I'm going so fast, with a puff, puff,

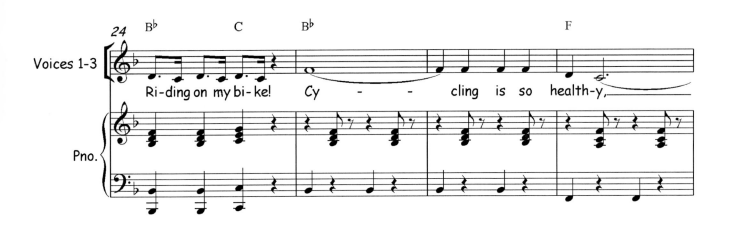

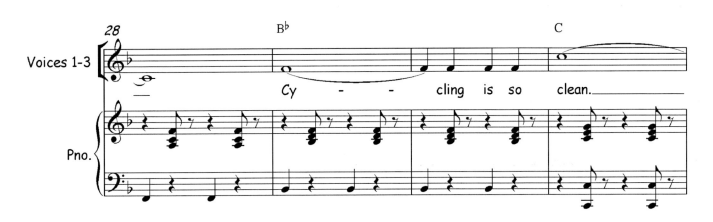

90

91

Battle for the Planet

Live for Tomorrow

Lyrics . . .

Planet Plenty

On Planet Plenty our motto is 'live for today'.
Drive around in our super spaceships and why mend things if you can throw
them away?
On Planet Plenty having fun is the only way.
Everyone's got swimming pools, open fires and hot tubs too.
No-one goes without on Planet Plenty!

On Planet Plenty we can do just as we please.
Stay up late having noisy parties, let our rubbish blow away in the breeze.
On Planet Plenty, our gardens are free from all disease.
Sprinklers on through day and night, fertilisers and pesticides,
No insects in sight on Planet Plenty!

We've got a King. And he gives us ideas only a king can bring.
Brains aren't his thing,
But he shows us how to drive spaceships faster, and how to tarmac the park.
And we keep the lights on all night, 'cos he's scared of the dark.
We've got a Queen. And she's the loveliest queen that you have ever seen.
She's really keen on the latest gadgets, her plastic palace, and all her time in
the shops.
And we keep the heating on full 'cos she likes to be hot, on Planet Plenty.

Repeat second verse.

The Heat is On

The heat is on, and getting hotter every day.
It's getting far too hot to work, this heat is driving us berserk,
Can't someone take the heat away?
All 'cross our planet it's the same, with extra heat comes extra rain,
I know that's sounding upside down, but that's what scientists have found,
The extra heat is stirring up the weather!

The heat is on, and getting hotter every hour.
It's getting far too hot to play, we'd rather lie down in the shade,
Or spend our time under a shower.
The weather's turning inside out, in one place storms, another, drought.
The extra energy around is making winds and gales abound,
Whilst here our lawn is turning rather brown!

The heat is on and getting hotter every minute.
It's getting far too hot to live, what we wouldn't give
For a freezer with us in it!
And at the North and South alike, the heat is melting all the ice,
And it won't take much common sense to guess what this has meant,
The oceans filled, and water levels risen.

The heat is on.

Acid Rain Blues

Acid rain. What's acid rain?
Acid rain. What's acid rain?
It's eating our trees. Acid rain.
Acid rain. Eating our trees.
Won't somebody help us. Who's there to help us?
Please.

I've got the acid rain blues,
It's eating into my shoes.
This rain ain't bringing good news.
We didn't know that we'd lose
Our verdant forests, our green dominion.
I've got the acid rain blues.
The leaves have all fallen, the branches are bare.
We look to the skies for their shelter, but their shelter's not there.
The trunks are discoloured, the colour of lead
We didn't appreciate the trees till the trees were dead!
(repeat)

I've got the acid rain blues.

Alone

There were times, long ago, when our planet was full of life,
Animals, birds, insects and fish in the rivers.
We were all part of a family; man had a place with them all,
Everyone equal, no-one left alone.

Now the birds never sing, now the fish never swim upstream,
Insects don't swarm; mammals lie dead in their burrows.
Take this chance; find out the reason, what has gone wrong?
If you don't make a change man will be left alone.

Spaceship Jam

My spaceship's shiny, it's really fast,
Zooming down the highway, it's such a blast,
It could do ninety, well that's the plan.
But there's traffic ahead, so I'm stuck here instead in a spaceship jam!
And I hear, beep, beep, beep etc.

My spaceship's curvy, it's really cool
It makes people stare when I drive it to school.
I like to go racing, I'm faster than you!
But there's no space above me, below or behind, there's a spaceship queue!
And I hear honk, honk, beep, beep etc.

My spaceship's gorgeous, I'm glad that it's mine.
Soaring off round the planet, looking real fine,
But today I'm not moving, I've gone into decline.
Cos I'm trapped here, I'm not going anywhere, stuck in a spaceship line!
And I hear parp, parp, parp, honk, honk, beep, beep etc.

CO$_2$ Monster

Well let us tell you 'bout a monster, a mean and heartless monster,
It's got no thought for anyone round here.
For it's just laughing as it's churning out the CO$_2$ each morning,
And we've got to catch it if we can.
Yes, we've got to hold that monster in our hands.

But where's it living?   Where do we find it?
How do we catch it? Will we recognise it?

You'll see the fire that comes from its snapping jaws, from its yellow tongue.
You'll catch the smell of its rancid, stale breath and you will want to run.
Its body's covered from head to toe with slimy ooze, but let it not confuse
you.
Underneath the slime he's fully protected with scales.
They're armour plated!
And it is filling the air with CO$_2$ 'cos it just doesn't care.

CO$_2$ monster, destroying our future. CO$_2$ monster, destroying our world.

But tell us something about its habits.
Give us a clue about how we should grab it.

It lives inside a fortress made of steel, no man has ventured in there.
It sleeps all day, for at night it's busy pumping out the poisoned air.
The carbon dioxide it makes in a bubbling vat, with many pipes attached.
And it uses its octopus arms to waft it outside. You'd better run and hide!
And it is filling the air with CO$_2$ 'cos he just doesn't care.

CO$_2$ monster, destroying our future. CO$_2$ monster, destroying our world.
CO$_2$ monster, destroying our future. CO$_2$ monster, destroying our world.

Drip Drip

Drip, drip, drip, drip
Never use a sprinkler, never use a sprinkler
Turn off the tap, turn off the tap,
Showers use much less water, showers use much less water.

Don't be the fools who let the pipes run dry.
Be known as those who kept the levels high,
You must preserve your liquid gold reserves,
Don't waste, don't let your planet die.

Showers use much less water, showers use much less water
Turn off the tap, turn off the tap,
Never use a sprinkler, never use a sprinkler
Drip, drip, drip, drip.

Recycle!

Recycle!
Recycle!
Recycle!
Newspapers, drink cans, cartons and veggie peelings,
catalogues, old magazines.
Recycle!
Plastic bottles, egg boxes, polystyrene.
Recycle!
Aluminium, sheets and curtains, tubs for your margarine.

Do you have to throw it away?
Can it come in useful another day?
We can save the planet if we all make a change.
So don't buy things that you don't need,
Re-use your stuff, give it away to people,
Or to make some compost using worms,
To change ketchup bottles into brooms,
Make a fleece from plastic you have used – Recycle!

Reduce! Re-use! Recycle!
Hedge clippings, envelopes, wood shavings, clean clothes
Duvet covers and shoes.
Recycle!
Medicine bottles, packaging for your shampoo.
Recycle!
Animal bedding, teabags and egg shells
Cardboard and yoghurt pots too.

Do you have to throw it away?
Can it come in useful another day?
We can save the planet if we all make a change.
So don't buy things that you don't need,
Re-use your stuff, give it away to people,
And for fewer trees to be cut down,
And for less rubbish buried underground,
And to save resources we have found – Recycle!

Save Energy

Turn off the lights, draw curtains tight,
You know it's right, and save energy.
It's better for you and me.
Turn down the heat, help make ends meet,
Switch off the TV, and save energy.
It's easy you'll see.

When you switch on the gas, or you use electricity, energy's coming to you.
But if you all use too much it will damage your planet,
So think what you're going to do.
The carbon dioxide you're forming goes up to the atmosphere,
Warming the world with a blanket of gases,
It means that your planet won't stop getting hotter and hotter,
and all of it's down to you!

Chorus twice

So put insulation in, think before switching on, don't overcharge your phone.
And keep your fridge door closed, have double glazed windows, and always
wash a full load.
And try out renewable energy, such as the wind or the sun,
and you'll see that your planet gets cleaner and you can be
sure that you're taking your world to a better state, through all your changes
at home!

Riding on my Bike!

Riding on my bike! Riding on my bike!
There's nothing like being on my bike with the wind rushing past my hair.
The fields tear past, 'cos I'm going so fast, with a puff, puff, and I'm nearly there.

Riding on my bike! Riding on my bike!
Cycling is so healthy, cycling is so clean.

Riding on my bike! Riding on my bike!
Ringing my bell, so everybody can tell that I'm coming, on my bicycle.
Saving on gas, so I'm saving on cash, and all they hear is, ting ting!

Riding on my bike!

Battle for the Planet

Extra paperwork and soaring overheads and profit margins are going to
take a dive.
Inconvenience, and working longer hours,
Why should we be made to change, and take the risk we lose our money?
Why not start with someone else? We'll think on the problem in good time.

We won't listen to your cries,
We are deaf to your complaints,
For our poor world cannot afford your point of view.
And you'll find to your surprise
In the battle for the planet
That we'll fight with grit and with determination,
Fight with fire, 'cos here's a fight we cannot lose.

Don't be silly, you're getting anxious,
There's just no need to get stressed and feel so blue.
Just relax, and let us do all the worrying,
And in a year or two, maybe three, we'll have some great ideas.
How we run our business is up to us, it isn't up to you.

This is just what we'd expect,
To be patronised and laughed at,
But you'll see that we won't give an inch to you.
We won't let our world be wrecked,
And the battle for the planet
Will be won by us, cos we're the future,
And we'll make you change your ways no matter what you do.

Live for Tomorrow

We're changing our ways, we'll live for tomorrow, not for today.
The changes we will make are here to stay.
We'll care for the land, we'll clean up the air, we'll show that we care.
We'll stop all the waste, our world will be safer now with us there.
We know what we've got to do.
Make our planet like brand new.
We're changing our ways, we'll live for tomorrow, not for today.
The changes we will make are here to stay.
We're changing our ways, we're changing our ways, see how we'll change.
We'll live for tomorrow, not for today, not for today.

Repeat

Choreography . . .

Choreography ideas for the instrumental sections of some of the songs, written by specialist dance teacher, Tracey Howkins.

The Heat is On

Over-riding feeling for this song is dignified and proud

During the instrumental:

5 steps to right diagonal front [slow, slow, quick, quick, slow] – arms in typical tango position.

Rock weight on to back foot, forward, back. Look to back then front. [Following the slow, slow, quick, quick, slow rhythm.]

4 walks around in a circle to the right, taking arms over head, joining wrists together with fingers spiky.

Slide right foot to side lunge – left arm high, right across body, draw up [bringing arms in front of chest fists together elbows lifted] and repeat to the other side.

4 x 3 steps, lift foot up to touch thigh at the back [right foot first], arms in front of chest fists together elbows lifted.

Moving to left diagonal back – 4 x step right foot across left, then left to side – taking left arm high, right arm across body with spiky fingers.

4 x steps in a circle to right – exaggerated sweep of the arms around – right arm high, left arm across body with spiky fingers. Return to original positions at this point.

Step feet together – both arms high, wrists together fingers spiky – then pull arms down in front of chest fists together elbows lifted.

At the end of the song children come together to slouch in a group looking hot and exhausted – they give a large puffy sigh!

Acid Rain Blues

Over-riding feeling to this song is 'cool'.

During the instrumental:

All facing the side

4 x step, touch foot to side of other foot – looking down with arm moving up to shoulder level in front [right foot first].

4 x steps moving sideways to face the back – right arm in straight line up to ceiling and back down again.

4 x steps – step side, side [right arm going out to the side shoulder height] and 2 to face the front [arms down].

4 x half note steps coming to original position – right hand finger clicking on the even counts.

Step – side, side, together – arms bent into waist. REPEAT to the other side.

Step forward pushing hip out. Turn to the back take 3 steps. REPEAT to face the front.

2 steps [feet apart on toes] – arms out in shoulder height line – 2 steps [bringing feet together]. REPEAT taking the arms up in parallel above head.

4 x steps coming forward to original place – feet apart.

Spaceship Jam

This dance is playful and has a more modern feel.

During the instrumental:

Hold a position for 4 counts

2 x step heel

Step right foot across left and swivel turn around to face the side – arms bent into the waist.

4 count body ripple facing side.

2 x step together using shoulder isolations – arms stretched towards the floor wrists flexed (facing side, travelling towards front).

2 x brush off shoulder with opposite hand.

2 walks forward to stand with arms folded ('giving attitude') for 2 counts.

4 walks to get back to where you started and face front.

Recycle!

During the instrumental:

Coke can group

4 x step close with hip wiggles
Step forward, step back, step to face the side – pause

[REPEAT along the side, back, side, ending up facing the front.]

Copper piping group

2 steps on tiptoes moving forward slightly – feet apart.
2 steps with bent knees – feet coming together.
REPEAT once
2 steps – out, out
2 steps – in, in
REPEAT 2 steps – out, out – pause

REPEAT three times

Plastic bottle group

3 x step forward, step back, step together - one to left side, back, right side. Step to face the front and pause.

3 x pause, then pencil jump – hold still through bar 4

REPEAT WHOLE ONCE.

Water bottle group

6 x The Twist (hips to left and then right) – step to face the left side – pause.

12 x jogging runs moving sideways to left – step to face the back – pause.

REPEAT WHOLE (across the back and down the side ending in original position).

Save Energy

Over-riding feeling to this song is relaxed and chilled.

During the instrumental:

4 x step together, step touch - scooping movement with arms.

4 x step, step behind, step touch – arm high, then arms low with a circular motion.

*2 x step forward, step, step touch – arms pushing forward.

*Step turn, step, finger click – *REPEAT this part.

Step to face the side – arms make a rainbow shape over head with hands shaking.

Riding on my Bike

Over-riding feeling to this song is cheerful and playful.

Movement for :

'There's nothing like . . .'

2 x grapevine - step side, behind, side, touch [right foot first]

4 x steps on the spot, brushing hand across face as if wind blowing, [right foot first]

Step right foot out to wide stance – use hand across eyes to show looking and sweep eyeline from left to right bending knees. REPEAT starting with the left foot.

Step forward taking arms up to parallel lines either side of head – drop arms and wiggle hips on 'puff, puff.'

Movement for:

'Cycling is so healthy . . .'

3 x steps with exaggerated ball change [step behind, step in front] – do this 4 times facing right side, back, left side, front.

Movement for:

'Ringing my bell . . .'

Facing front - step to side, step across in front, step to side, step across in front [left foot first]

1 slow turn – arms making a rainbow shape when facing front.

Spring step on the spot.

REPEAT to slow turn then do 2 small jumps with head tilts on the 'ting, ting'.

* The children may be split into groups to enable them to sing and dance in parts.

Battle for the Planet

Over-riding feeling for this song is exasperation and anger.

The Factory Owners (FO) on one side and the Children (Chn) on the other.

During the instrumental:

4 x jazz squares [4 steps moving forward, cross, side, side.] This is repeated 4 times facing the left side, back, right side and front – punching forward on the last 2 steps of each jazz square.

Both sides face each other.
8 x jogging runs with the FO and Chn slotting between each other, finish facing each other.

Chn bend down into ball shape, pause for 1 count, come up to standing and punch towards the FO.
As the Chn do this the FO do the same but start with the punch (a mock fight).

4 x walks to right then 4 x walks to the left, each side sizing each other up.

8 x jogging runs with each side returning to their original position.

Each side shake fists at each other x 4 times.

Links to QCA Schemes . . .

Links to QCA schemes of work – an overview	
Geography	Units 8, 11, 12, 16, 17, 20, 21 and 23 specifically. Supports knowledge and understanding of environmental change and sustainable development
Science	Units 3E, 4B, and 5-6H
Citizenship	Units 1, 2, 3, 6, 7 and 9
Dance (as part of PE)	Aspects of Units 3, 4 and 5

**Music QCA Unit 8 Ongoing skills –
the heart of the music curriculum for Years 3 and 4.**
Many of the learning objectives are covered in part by most of the songs.
The ones shown are the most directly connected.

Learning Objective	Song
To develop their singing voices	Planet Plenty, Acid Rain, Alone, CO_2 Monster, Save Energy
To use known songs to develop control of pulse and rhythm	Spaceship Jam, Drip Drip, Recycle!, Riding on my Bike
To develop awareness of simple structures	Alone, Recycle!
To recognise changes in, and to control, pitch	Planet Plenty, The Heat is On, Save Energy, Riding on my Bike
To learn about staff notation (through instrumental performance)	Drip Drip, Recycle!
To learn about how to express the meaning of songs	Acid Rain, CO_2 Monster, Battle for the Planet, Live for Tomorrow
To respond to structure in music through movement and dance	All the songs

Music QCA Unit 15 Ongoing skills – the heart of the music curriculum for Years 5 and 6.	
Learning Objective	**Song**
To learn about breathing, dynamics and accuracy of pitch	All songs, if focusing on posture and the singing face.
To learn how to improve tone production and use diction and other vocal techniques	The Heat is On, Acid Rain, CO_2 Monster, Drip, Drip, Recycle!, Riding on my Bike
To learn about pulse, rhythm and metre	Planet Plenty, Alone, Save Energy, Battle for the Planet, Live for Tomorrow
To learn about phrase and other musical structures	Alone, Spaceship Jam, Recycle!
To extend their control and understanding of pitch	All songs if sung in parts
To learn how to make expressive use of elements and techniques, and develop their performances.	All songs
To respond physically to music with understanding of musical features	All songs

Additional teaching notes for music . . .

Song	Teaching points, vocal challenges, and links to QCA stand alone units of work
Planet Plenty	2 part harmony
The Heat is On	Tango 2 part harmony
Acid Rain	Blues 2 part harmony Unit 19
Spaceship Jam	Rock and roll 3 part harmony Unit 10
Alone	4 part round Unit 17
CO_2 Monster	Ostinato (repeated pattern) 2 part harmony Unit 10
Drip, Drip	Gamelan (music from Bali) Pitched percussion 4 part harmony through ostinati Units 10, 11, 12, 17
Recycle!	Junk percussion Unison articulation of fast words Units 10, 16
Save Energy	Two part harmony
Riding on my Bike	3 part harmony through partner songs Unit 17
Battle for the Planet	2 part harmony through partner songs Unit 19
Live for Tomorrow	Calypso 2 part harmony

Cross Curricular Links . . .

Geography

'To help children to develop an informed concern about the quality of the environment and the future of the human habitat. To thereby enhance children's sense of responsibility for the care of the Earth and its people.' (DFES - Aims and Purposes of Geography)

The piece is aimed at supporting environmental education in school, and could be the basis of a whole key stage project on the environment.

Although Planet Plenty is a mythical planet, the issues that its people face are similar to those on Earth. Children could be encouraged to compare the way that the inhabitants of Planet Plenty and those of the Earth care for their worlds. What steps could the children take to reduce their impact on the environment? Are they more like the Plentarians or the Pleasantites?

Science

There are also links to the environmental education content in the science curriculum. For instance, the interdependence of living things, and how the environment, and thus habitats, need to be protected.

Citizenship

The citizens of Planet Plenty learn how their choices have affected their planet's environment. They have to listen to other's points of view, and make their choices more informed in the light of other people's experience.

Dance

The dance included within Planet Plenty shows regard to the National Curriculum for PE, with dance being one of the six activities to cover. Building upon their progress from Key Stage 1, the dance work in the show encourages children to develop their knowledge and skills whilst exploring styles from other cultures and places. It allows children to work towards the NC Level 4 attainment target *'Their performance shows precision, control and fluency, and that they understand tactics and composition.'*

Specific choreography ideas for the instrumental sections of some of the songs are included on pages 119-125, but other more general teaching ideas are:

Unit 4 – Encourage children to explore how to communicate character and narrative when moving on their own, with a partner or in a group.

Unit 5 – Help children to identify the dynamics of the movement, e.g. the speed and weight, and the spatial qualities of the movement, the way they fill the space around them with their bodies that are specific to the dance style.

Unit 5 – Teach the children to perform with clear starting and finishing positions. Encourage them to convey the mood and feeling of the dance. Help them to be sensitive to the musical accompaniment and to keep in time with it when performing.

Accompanying CD . . .

Produced by Phillip Sheppard
Sound Engineer – Roberto Borzoni
Saxophone – Tasha Smith
Piano – Jane Smith

Members of Seer Green CE Combined School Choir:
Jagger Barnett, Tiffany Branscombe, Bethany Chadwick, George Chilcott,
Sam Curtis, Kate Dransfield, Harriet Flashman, Hannah Grout, Zoe Heard,
Oliver Howkins, Sammy Isaacs-Johnson, Natalie Lawrence, Alexandra Laven,
Jonathon Ledgar, Megan McNeil, Paige Morgan, Grace Robin, Camilla Roy,
Niki Shah, Monica Thakor, Amy Thomson, Megan Turner, Sasha Warren,
Emily Wilson.

With singing
Track 1	Planet Plenty
Track 2	The Heat is On
Track 3	Acid Rain Blues
Track 4	Alone
Track 5	Spaceship Jam
Track 6	CO_2 Monster
Track 7	Drip, Drip
Track 8	Recycle
Track 9	Save Energy
Track 10	Riding on my Bike
Track 11	Battle for the Planet
Track 12	Live for Tomorrow

Without singing
Track 13	Planet Plenty
Track 14	The Heat is On
Track 15	Acid Rain Blues
Track 16	Alone
Track 17	Spaceship Jam
Track 18	CO_2 Monster
Track 19	Drip, Drip
Track 20	Recycle
Track 21	Save Energy
Track 22	Riding on my Bike
Track 23	Battle for the Planet
Track 24	Live for Tomorrow

Also available from:

PUBLISHING

Romancing Mary (FTRAW01)
    by Alan Wright

Cinder-Ellie at the Hoedown (FTRMP03)
    by Heather Butler

Baby Christmas and the Time Pilots (FTRAW03)
    by Alan Wright

The Ultimate Role Play Pack (FTRDD01)
    by Danny Davies

Order on-line @ **www.eprint.co.uk**